Galactic Adventures

LONDON, NEW YORK, MUNICH,
MELBOURNE, and DELHI

Editorial Lead Heather Jones
Senior Production Editor Clare McLean
Production Editor Kavita Varma
Managing Editor Catherine Saunders
Managing Art Editor Ron Stobbart
Brand Manager Lisa Lanzarini
Publishing Manager Simon Beecroft
Category Publisher Alex Allan
Production Controller Katherine Whyte

Lucasfilm
Executive Editor Jonathan W. Rinzler
Art Director Troy Alders
Keeper of the Holocron Leland Chee
Director of Publishing Carol Roeder
Reading Consultant Linda B. Gambrell, Ph.D.
004-180396-Oct/10

This edition published in Canada in 2010
Dorling Kindersley is represented in Canada by
Tourmaline Editions Inc
662 King Street West
Suite 304 Toronto, Ontario M5V 1M7

First published in the United States in 2005–2010 as
four separate titles: *Star Wars: Death Star Battles 2010,
Star Wars: Beware the Dark Side 2007, Star Wars:
Galactic Crisis! 2005, Star Wars: Epic Battles 2008*

A catalog record for this book is available
from the Library of Congress.

ISBN: 978-1-55363-153-8

Printed and bound in China by L Rex Printing Co., Ltd.

**Discover more at
www.dk.com**

www.starwars.com

Galactic Adventures

Contents

Death Star Battles

Written by Simon Beecroft

That's no moon!

You are flying through
deep space.
Suddenly a small
enemy fighter ship
shoots past.
Where did it
come from?
All you can see
is a small moon
up ahead.
Wait, that's no moon.
It is too big.
Quick, turn back!
Something is wrong with your ship.
It will not turn around!
You are being pulled toward the
most deadly battle station in the
galaxy: the Death Star.

The Death Star is the evil Empire's ultimate weapon. It has a superlaser that is powerful enough to destroy an entire planet with one gigantic blast.

The Death Star

The Death Star has a population of about 1.7 million people and over 400,000 droids.

How to build a Death Star

Only one man in the galaxy is evil enough to need a planet-destroying superweapon: Emperor Palpatine.

The Emperor is a vile Sith Lord. He rules the galaxy alongside Darth Vader and huge armies of deadly stormtroopers. The Emperor will do anything he can to increase his power.

He plans to use the Death Star to destroy his enemies and the Rebel Alliance.

Tarkin oversees construction of the Death Star with the Emperor and Darth Vader

Grand Moff Tarkin is one of the Emperor's top commanders. He masterminded the construction of the Death Star for Emperor Palpatine. He used a clever species of engineers, the Geonosians and he forced many Wookiee slaves and other prisoners to build the fearsome weapon.

Conference room

Grand Moff Tarkin and Darth Vader command the Death Star from the overbridge, where they make their sinister plans in a dark room in the overbridge. The Death Star has a special trained fighting force; Death Star Troopers.

Two Death Star Troopers stand guard
during top-level meetings. The Imperial
leaders sit around a black table with a
holoprojector in the middle for
displaying tactical holograms or maps.
During meetings Darth Vader
sometimes intimidates his officers by
using the dark side of the Force.

Fire when ready…

Grand Moff Tarkin and Darth Vader
have captured Princess Leia, an
important Rebel leader. They want her
to tell them the location of the Rebels'
hidden base. They threaten to destroy
her home planet Alderaan if she refuses.
Leia says the base is on a planet called
Dantooine. But then Tarkin decides to
destroy Alderaan to show the Rebels
what a powerful weapon the Empire has.

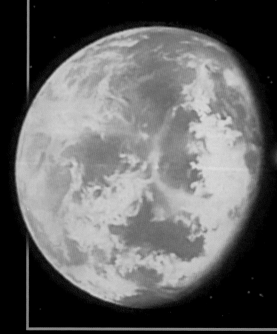

The disk-shaped superweapon blasts out eight beams of light that join together into one powerful laser beam. The small green planet is blown into space dust.

Superlaser
The Death Star's superlaser uses so much energy to fire that it takes 24 hours to recharge before it can be fired again.

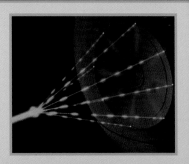

Trapped!

While Leia is being held prisoner on the
Death Star, Luke Skywalker is on his
way to Alderaan. He is traveling in a
starship called the *Millennium Falcon*.
With him are Jedi Knight Obi-Wan
Kenobi, captain Han Solo, a Wookiee
named Chewbacca, and two droids
C-3PO and R2-D2.

When they arrive where Alderaan used
to be, they see a TIE fighter. It heads
straight toward a small moon which
turns out to be the Death Star.

The Death Star uses an invisible tractor beam to grab hold of Luke's ship so it cannot escape. They are pulled into a docking bay within a mile-high trench that runs around the middle of the Death Star.

Deadly surface

The surface of the Death Star is covered with weapons, including 10,000 turbolaser guns and 2,500 laser cannons. 8,000 tractor beam projectors can trap any enemy ships that come too close.

Into the Death Star

The *Falcon* is forced to land in a giant hangar. An invisible shield across the entrance maintains the artificial atmosphere.

Docking bays

The Death Star has many docking bays for spaceships. Some are designed for visiting ships, others are hangars for Imperial fighters such as TIE.

Beside the ship is a large hole in the floor, which has an elevator to raise and lower ships for repairs.

Control room windows overlook the hangar. They are surrounded by stormtroopers.

Stormtroopers

Stormtroopers are the Empire's elite soldiers. They wear white helmets that cover their faces and suits of armor made up of 18 pieces.

Stormtroopers are armed with blaster pistols or blaster rifles.

A squad of stormtroopers boards the *Falcon*. They are looking for the crew. Luke and the others are hiding in secret compartments beneath the floor.

Tour of duty
At least 25,000 stormtroopers serve on the Death Star at any one time. They patrol every part of the enormous battle station.

I can't see in this helmet!

Han and Luke ambush two
stormtroopers and steal their armor.
Disguised as stormtroopers, they
discover that Princess Leia is a prisoner.

Turbolifts

Elevators, called turbolifts, connect all sectors of the Death Star. Turbolifts move up and down as well as side to side. Some turbolifts are reserved for officers.

Luke has a plan to rescue her.

They handcuff Chewbacca so they can pretend he is their prisoner.

Han and Luke try to look relaxed in their stormtrooper disguises as they wait for a turbolift to arrive.

Troops, bureaucrats, and robots move about, but most of them ignore the trio. Only a few glance at the giant Wookiee.

Prison break

Finally, Luke and Han find the prison
block in which Leia is being held.
But an Imperial officer becomes
suspicious and they have a blaster battle.
After Luke finds Leia, more stormtroopers
arrive, cutting off their only exit.
Han and Luke exchange fire with
the stormtroopers.

Interrogator droid
Imperial cell blocks
are horrible places.
Security cameras
spy on prisoners while
interrogator droids
electroshock them
to force them to
answer questions.

Leia has to think very fast now.
The only way out is a garbage chute!

Something is alive in here!

Luke, Leia, Han, and Chewbacca whiz
down the garbage chute and land in
a smelly, dirty trash compactor.
This is where garbage of every kind is
collected before being crushed and
dumped into space. It is totally sealed.

Dianoga serpent
Dianogas, or garbage
squids, live in trash
compactors, refuse pits
and sewers across the
galaxy, feeding on
scraps and rubbish.

When Han tries to blast his way out,
the laserbolt bounces around the small
metal room and nearly hits one of them.
Then they hear a frightening growl and
realize something is living in there.
Suddenly, a long tentacle grabs hold of
Luke and pulls him underwater!
The others think Luke is gone forever,
but the creature spits him out.
Then the walls start closing in.
They are going to be crushed!

Droids to the rescue

Luke shouts into his comlink to get help from C-3PO and R2-D2.

But C-3PO cannot answer because stormtroopers are searching the control room.

The droid tells them that Luke and the others are heading for the prison block level. The stormtroopers go after Luke, Han, and Chewbacca.

C-3PO finally hears Luke begging the droids to turn off the garbage masher. The droids can hear them screaming. They think that their friends are being crushed to death. Actually, they are whooping for joy because the walls have stopped closing in. Well done, R2-D2!

Desperate leap

As Luke and Leia are
trying to escape the deadly
stormtroopers, they run
through a doorway—and
nearly fall from a ledge to
their death. Below them is a
deep shaft that appears to go
on forever!

Luke fires at the stormtroopers
and Leia hits a switch that
shuts the door, leaving them
perched on the short ledge.
But the stormtroopers are
opening the door.

On the other side of the chasm, more
stormtroopers begin to blast at them.
Luke fires at the new enemies, but then
he has an idea.

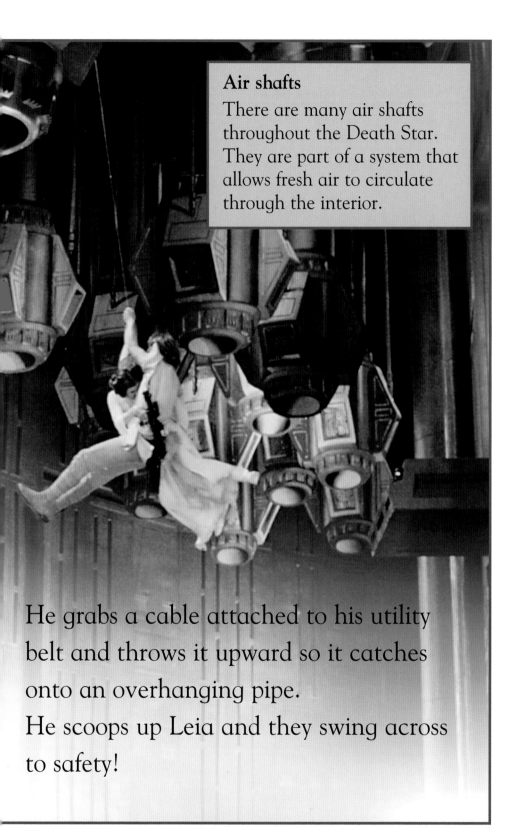

He grabs a cable attached to his utility belt and throws it upward so it catches onto an overhanging pipe.

He scoops up Leia and they swing across to safety!

Solo mission

Machines called reactor couplings power
the huge tractor beam.

This is the beam that is preventing
Han's ship from leaving the Death Star.
Obi-Wan knows that if he switches off
one of these machines, he will free
the *Falcon*.

He slips past stormtroopers using the
Force to stay hidden.

Obi-Wan finally reaches the reactor
coupling. It stands on a shaft inside
a trench that seems to be a hundred
miles deep.

The Jedi edges his way along a narrow
ledge that leads to a control panel.
He quickly turns off the machines.

Final duel

The most fearsome presence on the Death Star is Darth Vader. His black caped figure walking down the corridor is a terrifying sight. Vader can sense that Obi-Wan Kenobi is on the Death Star and tracks him down. They confront each other. Swoosh! Their lightsabers clash and spark!

Lost friendship
Darth Vader is a Sith Lord who was once Jedi Knight Anakin. Anakin is Luke's father. Obi-Wan was Anakin's Master until Anakin became a Sith. Anakin fought Obi-Wan, but lost. He has wanted revenge since then.

Luke watches Obi-Wan block Vader's every move, until the old Jedi Master stands still with a calm look on his face. Vader strikes down Kenobi with a single slash of his blade. Obi-Wan's cloak falls to the floor, but he is not in it.
Luke cries out, "No!" as Vader prods the empty robe with his foot.

We are not safe yet!

Thanks to Obi-Wan, the *Falcon* blasts off from the deadly Death Star. But TIE fighters give chase. Luke and Han work together, manning their turbolasers and blowing up all the enemy ships.

Han and Luke are relieved, but Leia thinks Tarkin has let them escape. Leia is right—Tarkin is tracking their ship. He still wants to find out the location of the Rebels' hidden base.

X-wings

X-wings are starfighters. They have four wings, called S-foils, which form the shape of an 'X'. They are made by a company called Incom.

Rebel attack

The Death Star is more powerful than half the entire firepower of the Imperial Starfleet. But the Rebels think they have found a way to destroy it.

Rebel pilots must use all their skill to fly

Rebel briefing
At the Rebel base on Yavin 4, the Rebels study the Death Star plans that R2-D2 has been carrying. Leia knows that the Rebels must act fast if they want to outsmart Vader.

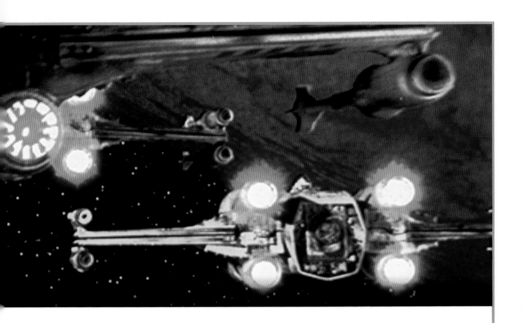

along a narrow tunnel on the surface
of the Death Star.

At the end of the tunnel is an exhaust
port. If they can fire a laser bolt right
into this tiny hole, the bolt will
penetrate the main reactor.

This will start a chain reaction that
should destroy the station.

The Rebels hope that their ships are
small enough to avoid the Death Star's
outer defenses, which are designed to
stop large-scale assaults.

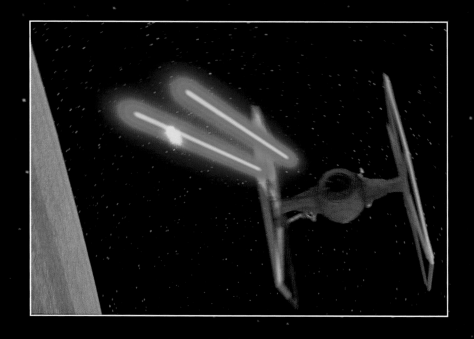

Turbolaser defense

The Death Star has powerful
turbolasers, but the starfighters are
nimble. The Death Star's defenses
are also not strong enough against
the Force.

When Obi-Wan tells Luke to "use the
Force" instead of his targeting
computer, Luke fires two proton
torpedos into the Reactor Core.

The battle station is destroyed before it can attack the Rebel base. But the sinister Emperor will not let this stop him. He has a plan...

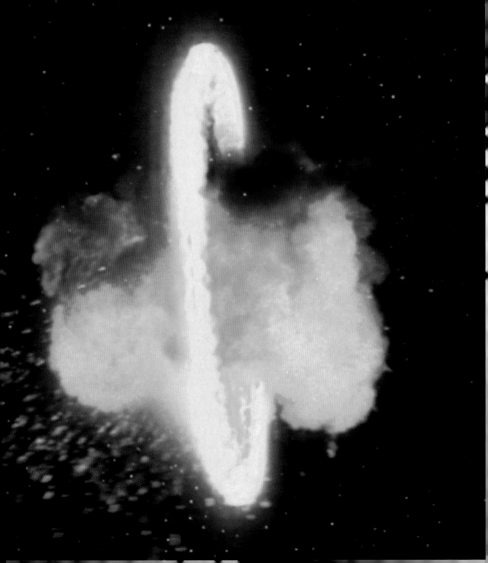

The second Death Star

After the destruction of the Death Star at the Battle of Yavin, Emperor Palpatine orders the construction of a second Death Star. This battle station is even larger than the first, with thousands more turbolasers. The second Death Star also has a planet-destroying superlaser—but it can be recharged in only three minutes. This superlaser can also fire at small targets, such as enemy ships. It is more powerful and accurate.

The Emperor is sure that, this time, he will crush forever the Rebel rebellion.

Emperor Palpatine arrives

The Emperor's personal shuttle lands on the new Death Star. He has arrived to inspect the new battle station.

He is greeted by Darth Vader.
Hundreds of stormtroopers line
up and the Imperial Red Guards
bow to him.

The Emperor wants this Death
Star to look unfinished in order to
trick the Rebels into attacking.
In fact, its superlaser is already a
dangerous weapon!

When the Rebels attack, the
Emperor intends to destroy their
fleet once and for all!

The throne room

Emperor Palpatine has a private command center on the second Death Star. It is located on top of a 100-storey tower on the North Pole of the superweapon.

Security is very high around the throne room to stop any intruders.

Each entrance has a trap and is guarded by the Emperor's Imperial Guards.

There is a docking rig for the Emperor's personal shuttle and a sleep chamber that monitors his health.

Emperor Palpatine sits on a large throne. From there he contemplates his most horrible plan—to turn Luke to the dark side! He is sure that Luke will kill Vader, Luke's father, and therefore become a Sith Lord and the Emperor's new apprentice.

Final battle

The Rebels decide to attack the second Death Star because it seems weak and unprotected, just as the Emperor planned. The Rebel fleet is led by Han's

friend Lando Calrissian, who is flying the *Falcon*. They don't know it is a trap. Meanwhile, Palpatine tricks Luke into battle with Darth Vader. Luke defeats his father—but refuses to kill him.
So, the Emperor unleashes unstoppable Sith lightning at Luke. At the last moment, Darth hurls the Emperor into an abyss, saving Luke's life.

Most powerful Jedi
Because Luke feels compassion for his father, Darth Vader, he reveals himself to be the most powerful Jedi of them all.

Battle of Endor

A Rebel team, led by Han Solo and Princess Leia, destroys the shield generator protecting the Death Star. This allows the *Falcon* to fly into its interior, chased by TIE fighters.

Lando and his friends blast away at the main reactor.

The Death Star explodes!

Emperor Palpatine is dead.

All over the galaxy, people celebrate their new freedom.

Big explosion
The second Death Star becomes a ball of flames and the *Falcon* flies away. The Rebels have won!

Glossary

Ambush
A surprise attack made by people from a hiding place.

Armor
Protective clothing.

Artificial
Fake or not real.

Bureaucrat
An office worker.

Chain Reaction
An event that leads to another important event happening.

Engineer
A person who designs and makes machinery or vehicles.

Enormous
Unusually big.

Fearsome
Very frightening.

The Force
A mysterious energy that can be used for good or evil.

Geonosian
Insectoid race from the planet Geonosis.

Hangar
A large, warehouse building or room for housing spaceships or vehicles.

Holoprojector
A device that projects a hologram.

Nimble
Fast and able to change direction quickly.

Reactor Coupling
The system that powers the tractor beams.

Sinister
Very bad, mysterious, and scary.

Sith Lord
A leader of the evil Siths who use the dark side of the Force.

Slave
Someone who is owned by a master and is forced to do everything they are told to.

Stormtrooper
Members of the Emperor's personal army.

Tentacle
The long, flexible legs and arms of a creature with many limbs.

Terrifying
Extremely scary and frightening.

Tractor Beam
A beam that can pull one object toward another.

STAR WARS

BEWARE THE
DARK SIDE

Written by Simon Beecroft

The Force
The Force is an invisible energy created by all living things. A few people with special powers can control the Force. The Force is mostly a good energy, but it also has a dark side that can be used for evil.

Faces of Evil

A long time ago, the galaxy was ruled by an evil man named Darth Sidious (pronounced SID-EE-US). He was also known as Emperor Palpatine (pronounced PAL-PA-TEEN). He used fear, corruption, and the dark side of the Force to rule his evil Empire.

Emperor Palpatine

Darth Sidious's special abilities made him very powerful. He used the dark side of the Force to control people's minds and events. He also used the dark side to throw heavy objects with his mind, and to fire a deadly lightning from his fingers.

In these pages, you will meet many villains who used the dark side of the Force to do terrible things. You will also meet evildoers who did not use the Force, but who were still on the side of darkness. Finally, you will meet the brave few who dared to stand up to the dark side.

The Jedi order
Jedi Master Obi-Wan Kenobi said that the Force "surrounds us, penetrates us, and binds the galaxy together". The Jedi are a group of individuals who devote their lives to using the Force for good. The Jedi protect people and keep peace in the galaxy.

Sith Lord

Darth Sidious was a Sith Lord.
The Sith had been around for many
centuries. The first Sith was a Jedi
who turned to the dark side. Others
followed him. Together they tried to
destroy the Jedi. The Sith even tried
to kill each other because they were
so full of evil and hatred. The Jedi
thought they had destroyed the Sith.
But, one Sith survived. He took an
apprentice and went into hiding.
Since then, the Sith have plotted
revenge on the Jedi.

The Sith were the Jedi's most feared enemies. The Sith used the dark side of the Force to gain terrible powers. Like the Jedi, they fought with a lightsaber, which is a sword whose blade is made of pure energy. The Sith and the Jedi were the only people in the galaxy who used lightsabers. The lightsaber was the ancient weapon of the Jedi, but since the Sith were once Jedi, they used them too.

Lightsabers
The handle contains special crystals that make the energy blade appear when needed. Jedi lightsaber blades are either blue, green, or purple.

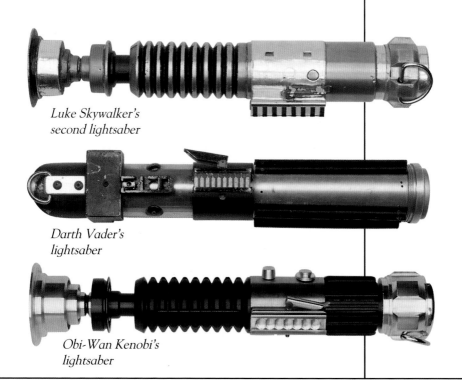

Luke Skywalker's
second lightsaber

Darth Vader's
lightsaber

Obi-Wan Kenobi's
lightsaber

Sith Powers

The Sith believed that the dark side of the Force was more powerful than the light. Turning to the dark side seemed to bring results quickly, while the Jedi had to patiently study the light side of the Force for many years. The Sith also rejected the Jedi's teachings that emotions must be controlled. They used anger and hatred to become stronger, but the Sith had no loyalty and were often destroyed by the dark side.

Evil temptation
The Jedi understood that the dark side was a powerful temptation for all Jedi. Most managed to resist it, but a few gave in to its evil powers.

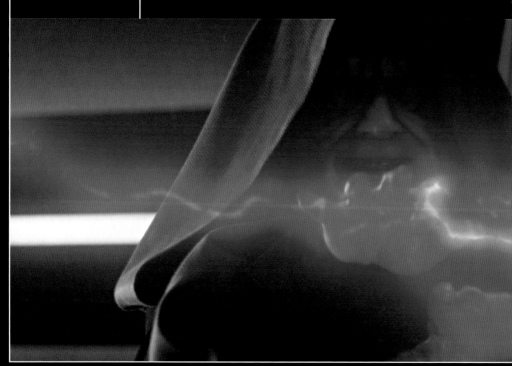

In battle, the Sith tried to crush their opponents with heavy objects, which they threw using their dark side energies.

The dark side of the Force gave the Sith powers that the Jedi did not have. One of them was deadly Force lightning. They could fire it from their fingers at an opponent. However, this power was very dangerous and could also harm the user.

Force lightning
When Sidious attacked a Jedi called Mace Windu with Force lightning, Mace threw it back at Sidious. The lightning hit Sidious's face and scarred it forever.

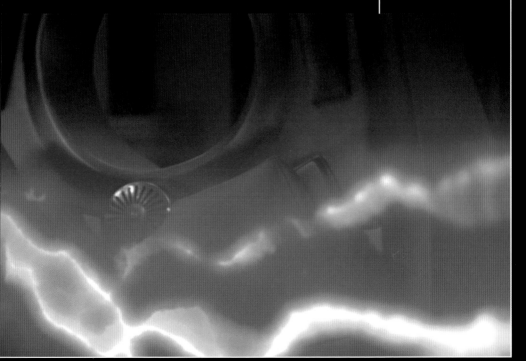

The Phantom Menace

Before Darth Sidious became Emperor of the galaxy, he was a popular politician called Senator Palpatine. At this time, the galaxy was at peace and laws were made in the Senate. All the different planets had a voice in the Senate and large armies were outlawed.

Palpatine secretly wanted to take over the galaxy. He planned to destroy the Senate and build a massive army so that he could force every planet to do what he wanted.

No one suspected that Palpatine was really a Sith Lord. After he secretly started a war in the galaxy, Palpatine convinced the Senate to make him their leader, the Supreme Chancellor. Then he gave himself the power to make all the decisions. Finally, he crowned himself Emperor. Now the dark side ruled the galaxy.

The Senate
The Senate was a gigantic circular building on the galaxy's capital planet, Coruscant.

Secret Sith
Palpatine hid his true Sith identity from the Senate.

Jedi Defenders

When the Sith revealed themselves after two thousand years in hiding, only the Jedi had the powers to face them. The Jedi vow to use their Force powers only to do good. The good side of the Force is known as the light side.

Learning to use the light side of the Force takes many years. Those who become Jedi begin training as young children. They must leave their families behind and live in the Jedi Temple on a big planet.

Yoda
Yoda was the wisest Jedi of all. He was hundreds of years old when the Sith reappeared.

The Jedi learn to control their emotions so that they can remain calm and practical in all situations. The Jedi seek to keep the Force in balance in the galaxy, which means that they must stop those who seek to use the dark side.

The Jedi can actually listen to the Force telling them that there is trouble happening somewhere. This is known as a disturbance in the Force. It means there's a problem some place in the galaxy— and the Jedi must find it and do whatever they can to stop it.

Obi-Wan
Obi-Wan Kenobi was a powerful Jedi. While the Sith ruled the galaxy, Obi-Wan went into hiding. Yoda also went into hiding.

Jedi Council
The wisest, most experienced Jedi sat on the Jedi High Council. Before the Sith attacked, Yoda felt great disturbances in the Force, but even he was not able to see where the threat came from.

Masked man
Vader's armor and breathing equipment were created in a secret medical facility.

Vader uncovered
Vader removed his helmet only in a special isolation chamber. Mechanical arms lifted the helmet from his scarred head.

Darth Vader

Darth Vader ruled the galaxy alongside Darth Sidious. Vader was also a Sith Lord. His knowledge of the dark side of the Force made him a powerful and dangerous figure. Vader would kill anyone who got in his way or disobeyed him, even his own generals. He used his Force powers to strangle people without even touching them.

Darth Vader always wore a black suit of armor and a black mask because his body had been almost destroyed in a great battle. His armor and mask contained breathing equipment and life-support systems to keep him alive. The wheezing sound of Vader's artificial breathing was enough to strike terror into the mind of anyone he approached.

Space fighter
Vader flew his own fighter ship into combat. He was a very daring pilot.

Lightsaber duel
Vader was a merciless opponent in battle, and did not hesitate to cut down his former Master, Obi-Wan Kenobi.

Boyhood
Anakin was
born on a poor
desert planet
called Tatooine.
He spent his
boyhood as a
slave until a Jedi
Master named
Qui-Gon Jinn
rescued him.

Anakin Skywalker

Before he became a Sith Lord, Darth Vader was a Jedi called Anakin Skywalker. Anakin was one of the most talented Jedi ever. His Force powers were incredibly strong, but Anakin was impatient.

He wanted to become more powerful than any other Jedi.

Palpatine befriended Anakin and began to plant ideas in his mind.

Tragic death
When Anakin
joined the Jedi,
he had to leave
his mother
behind. He
never forgave
himself when he
could not
prevent her
from dying at
the hands of
a vicious species
called Sand
People.

He convinced Anakin to join him on the dark side and train to be a Sith. Palpatine told Anakin that the dark side of the Force was more powerful than the light side. He even told Anakin that he would be able to stop his wife from dying. Anakin wanted this more than anything, so he rejected his Jedi training and joined Palpatine.

When Anakin joined the dark side, he killed many Jedi. He even fought his best friend, Obi-Wan Kenobi. On the edge of a lava river, Anakin and Obi-Wan fought fiercely until Obi-Wan managed to strike down his former friend. Anakin fell near the red-hot lava and burst into flames. Palpatine rescued him, and re-built his badly burned body with robotic parts and a suit of armor—and Darth Vader was born!

Padmé Amidala
Anakin secretly married the Senator for Naboo, Padmé Amidala, even though the Jedi are forbidden to marry.

Maul

Each Sith Master chose a single apprentice, whom he trained in the dark side. Sidious first chose a savage alien from the planet Iridonia. Given the Sith name Darth Maul, he served his master obediently, although he was only waiting for the day when he would take Sidious's place. Maul had horns on his head and yellow eyes. His face was tattooed with dark side symbols. Maul's weapon was a double-bladed lightsaber.

Sith ship
Maul's spaceship could make itself appear invisible to others.

Speeder
Maul also used a speeder that flew along just above the ground. It had an open cockpit.

When two Jedi named Qui-Gon Jinn (pronounced KWY-GONN-JIN) and Obi-Wan Kenobi (pronounced OH-BEE-ONE KEN-OH-BEE) started to upset Sidious's plans, he sent Maul to kill them. The fight took place on the edge of a giant power generator on Palpatine's home planet, Naboo. The Jedi were not prepared for such a ferocious attack. Qui-Gon was killed, but Obi-Wan defeated the deadly Sith apprentice.

Sith Master
Sidious kept in contact with his apprentice using a hologram transmitter.

Count Dooku

Sidious needed a new apprentice after Obi-Wan killed Darth Maul on Naboo. His search led him to Count Dooku, who was once a Jedi Master. Although he joined the Jedi order at a young age, Dooku was interested in the dark side and wanted power to change things quickly. When Dooku joined Sidious, he took the new Sith name—
Darth Tyranus.

Weapon
Tyranus's weapon was a lightsaber with a curved handle. His special moves could surprise even the most experienced Jedi.

Count Dooku

For many years, Dooku had been encouraging planets and business organizations to leave the Senate and build droid armies. He told them that this would make the galaxy a better place. In reality he was doing only what Sidious told him to do. He did not know what Sidious's true plans were.

Sidious eventually betrayed Dooku and allowed him to be killed by Anakin Skywalker. Sidious knew that the powerful and gifted Anakin would be a more useful Sith apprentice than Dooku.

Force lightning
Like Sidious, Tyranus used Force lightning to deadly effect.

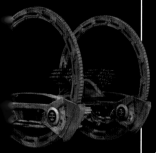

Droid Army

Count Dooku had persuaded many planets and organizations to buy powerful droid armies. The footsoldiers were blaster-wielding battle droids while heavily armored super battle droids provided backup. Hailfire droids rolled across the battlefields, each equipped with deadly cannon or missile launchers. Deadly machines called droideka were used on special missions.

Hailfire droids
Hailfire droids are shaped like massive wheels. They can race across flat ground or shallow lakes, flattening anything in their path.

Tri-fighter
Tri-fighters seek out and hunt down enemy ships in space, training their deadly nose cannons on their prey.

Heavily armed droid ships were also used for space battles. They included vulture droids, which could also walk along the ground, and tri-fighters. Swarms of tiny buzz droids attached themselves to enemy ships. Although they were very small, their cutting and sawing arms could inflict serious damage.

Spider droids
Spider droids go into battle equipped with heat-seeking missiles.

General Grievous

With the outbreak of war in the galaxy, many brutal fiends joined the Sith Lords. One such recruit was General Grievous, a warlord whose battle-scarred body had been rebuilt with cyborg parts. The only parts of his original body left were his reptile-like eyes and his inner organs, which were protected by armor. Although he was more machine than man, Grievous would kill anyone who called him a droid.

Bodyguards
Grievous was accompanied by droid bodyguards, who were equipped with deadly energy staffs.

Grievous became Supreme Commander of the droid armies. Dooku taught Grievous to use a lightsaber, although Grievous could not use the Force like the Sith and Jedi.

Grievous had a long-standing grudge against the Jedi, and took the lightsabers of any Jedi he killed. In battle, Grievous could split his two arms into four, each of which could wield a lightsaber. He also used a deadly blaster and a powerful energy staff, which delivered fatal electric shocks to his opponents.

Final battle
Grievous was no match for the combined power of the Jedi Obi-Wan Kenobi and Anakin Skywalker.

Clone Soldiers

Although Sidious had started a war in the galaxy, he didn't want either side to win it. He wanted the war to go on just long enough for him to bring the Sith to power. He made sure that the Republic had an army of its own, so that each side was evenly matched. The Republic army consisted of well-trained clone soldiers and a variety of battle tanks, plus cannons, gunships, and space assault ships.

Special training
Each clone trooper was an identical copy of a single "supreme soldier" named Jango Fett. Each clone was grown in a factory and trained for combat from birth.

Battle vehicles
In battle, clone troopers operated several kinds of tank and flew armed gunships.

For many battles, the clone soldiers fought on the side of the Republic. The Jedi generals did not know that the clone soldiers were programmed to be loyal to Sidious. When Sidious gave a special signal, the clone soldiers turned on their Republic masters, showing no mercy.

Weapons
Clone troopers carried powerful blasters and rifles.

Stormtroopers

When the war was over, Darth Sidious ruled the galaxy as Emperor Palpatine, and the clone soldiers became his personal army. He renamed them stormtroopers and forced many millions of human males to join their ranks. Military Academies were formed in which new recruits were trained to be foot soldiers or more specialized troops, such as pilots or scouts. The stormtroopers were trained to be totally loyal to the Empire.

Armor
Stormtrooper armor protected the soldier inside from weapon and bomb blasts.

Stormtrooper

The stormtroopers could not be bribed or persuaded into betraying the Emperor. People everywhere learned to fear the sinister white-armored troops.

Snowtroopers
Some stormtroopers wore specialized armor to protect them from the cold on freezing planets. They were called snowtroopers.

Vader's son
Luke was raised on Anakin's home planet, Tatooine, by his uncle and aunt.

Vader's daughter
Leia was raised on the planet Alderaan. She became a Princess—and a secret member of the Rebel Alliance.

Empire and Rebels

When Darth Sidious came to power, a dark age began in the galaxy—the Empire. As Emperor Palpatine, Sidious used his massive armies to terrify the galaxy and to stop anyone from rising against him.

Nevertheless, a secret opposition was formed, called the Rebel Alliance. The most famous Rebels were the children of Darth Vader, Luke and Leia.

When Anakin Skywalker turned to the dark side, he did not know that his wife, Padmé Amidala, was pregnant with twins. Tragically, Padmé died while giving birth. The twins were hidden away in separate places, so that Anakin would not find out about them.

Rebel Alliance
Leia and the Rebel Alliance plan an attack on the Empire from their secret base on the planet Yavin 4.

Han Solo
The Rebels welcomed any support they could get, even from former smugglers like Han Solo and Chewbacca.

Warrior upbringing
Jango was an orphan. He was raised by a legendary warrior army, thought to be the most dangerous in the galaxy.

Equipment
Jango wore a protective helmet to hide his identity. A jetpack allowed him to blast into the air and escape.

Jango Fett

The first clone troopers were cloned from a single "supreme warrior." He was a man named Jango Fett. Jango made his living as a bounty hunter. This means that he was paid to hunt criminals and outlaws. Darth Tyranus knew of his unbeatable combat skills and recruited him for the secret clone-army project.

Jango Fett

Jango also carried out certain special missions for the Sith Lords. For example, he would assassinate any public figures that stood between the Sith Lords and their ultimate goal of ruling the galaxy. One such person was the good Senator Padmé Amidala. Thankfully, Padmé survived the attempts on her life, and the Jedi pursued Jango. Eventually, Jango was killed in a large battle between the Republic army and the droid army.

Jetpack
Jango uses his jetpack to attack Jedi Obi-Wan from above.

Flame thrower
Jango fires his deadly wrist-mounted flame thrower.

Airspeeder
When Zam needed to make a fast getaway, she jumped into her fast, green airspeeder.

Zam Wesell

Jango Fett had many contacts in the criminal underworld. One such contact was the hired assassin Zam Wesell. Zam was an alien whose species could shape-shift, which meant that she could change her body shape to imitate other species. This was useful when she needed to blend in with another planet's species without being noticed.

Jango hired Zam to carry out the daring murder of the politician Senator Padmé Amidala. First Zam tried to blow up the Senator's spaceship. Then, she released deadly insects called kouhuns into Padmé's bedroom while she slept, but her Jedi bodyguards were able to stop the attack in time. Zam was chased by the Jedi Obi-Wan Kenobi and Anakin Skywalker. They managed to capture her, but before she could give anything away, she was shot by a mysterious figure in the shadows—Jango Fett.

Jedi protector
Obi-Wan was trying to protect Senator Amidala.

True face
When shape-shifters die, they return to their own body shape.

Boba Fett

When Jango Fett was killed in battle, he left a young son named Boba. Young Boba had spent his whole life learning from his father, so when he grew up, he too became a bounty hunter. Boba inherited his father's armor and weapons, and became the best bounty hunter in the galaxy. Boba often worked for Darth Vader, tracking down enemies of the Empire.

When Darth Vader learned that he had a son, he wanted to track him down and see if he could turn him to the dark side. He would have liked to rule the galaxy alongside his son.

Like father, like son
Boba Fett is an exact, unaltered clone of his father, Jango.

Secret weapons
Boba's armor conceals a deadly flame thrower and powerful rocket dart launchers.

Vader employed Boba Fett
to find and capture Luke,
but Luke was firmly
on the side of
good. He had
begun to train as a
Jedi and refused to
turn to the dark side.

Boba was eventually
defeated during a battle with Luke
Skywalker and his allies. Boba Fett's
jetpack was damaged, causing it to
malfunction. It sent the bounty
hunter soaring into the air, out of
control. Fett finally tumbled to his
death into the ravenous jaws of
a giant desert creature called
the Sarlacc.

**Armed
spaceship**
Boba traveled in
his father's ship,
"Slave I".
The ship was
full of weapons.

Possible escape
Some people
believe that
Boba managed
to escape from
the stomach of
the Sarlacc.

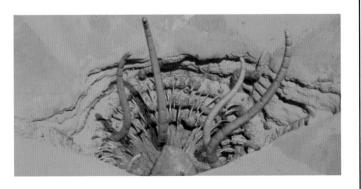

Jabba the Hutt

Another of Boba Fett's employers was a crime lord named Jabba the Hutt. This repellent slug-like creature was the leader of a large crime empire responsible for all kinds of shady deals, including murder, theft, and fraud. Jabba lived in a palace on the desert planet Tatooine. He shared his palace with assorted gangsters, assassins, smugglers, corrupt officials, low-life entertainers, and servants.

Jabba paid Boba Fett to bring him a smuggler who owed him money. That smuggler was Han Solo, who had become friends with Luke and Leia

Skywalker. When Han was captured and brought to Jabba, Leia set out with Chewbacca to rescue Han. When she was also captured, it was up to Luke to rescue all his friends. During Luke's rescue mission, Leia was able to wrap a chain around Jabba's neck and defeat him.

Bib Fortuna
Bib Fortuna ran Jabba's palace for him. He had a large head tail, sharp teeth, and scary red eyes.

Pet monster
Jabba kept a ferocious rancor monster in a cellar pit. Sometimes he fed it human captives for fun.

Rogues and Villains

Even before the Empire took control, parts of the galaxy were wild and lawless. On remote planets like Tatooine, highly dangerous Podraces were organized, although they were officially banned. Slavery was also common. When the Jedi Qui-Gon visited Tatooine, he met a slave dealer named Watto. Watto owned Anakin Skywalker and his mother, Shmi. Anakin and Shmi both worked for Watto in his junk shop.

Informer
Garindan was a low-life informer who lived on Tatooine.

Watto
Watto made Anakin and Shmi work very hard.

Under the Empire, crime was often rewarded. The Empire relied on spies to report suspicious behavior. Often, it forced officials to do its shady business.

When Darth Vader wanted to capture Luke Skywalker, he threatened to shut down an entire city if its leader, Lando Calrissian, did not lure Luke into a trap. When Vader broke his promise, Lando helped Luke and joined the Rebels.

Calrissian
Lando Calrissian had great charm.

Greedo
Greedo was a small-time hitman hired to kill Han Solo.

Imperial Might

The Empire kept control of the galaxy with its gigantic army of stormtroopers and a fleet of warships

Heavy weapons
Star Destroyers were armed with many powerful weapons.

that patrolled all the major space routes. The biggest warship was Darth Vader's personal ship, the "Executor." The "Executor" led a fleet of Star Destroyers.

Each Star Destroyer had enough firepower to destroy entire planets. Swarming around these big ships were countless smaller TIE-fighters, each piloted by a fighter pilot.

When the Empire discovered a Rebel secret base on the ice planet Hoth, it sent in massive walking tanks called AT-ATs. Pilots controlled the tanks from a cockpit in the head. Until the battle of Hoth, AT-ATs were thought to be unbeatable in battle, but the Rebels toppled them by wrapping cables around their legs.

Scout walkers
Smaller AT-ST, or scout walkers, patrolled many planets.

Sinister spy
A probe droid spotted the Rebel base on Hoth and informed the Empire.

Death Star

The Death Star was the Emperor's most terrifying superweapon. It was the size of small moon, but it was actually one of the largest starships ever built. Its gigantic superlaser weapon could destroy entire planets. To demonstrate its enormous power,

the Empire used it to destroy the planet of Alderaan. This was the planet on which Darth Vader's daughter, Leia, had lived most of her life.

Fatal flaw
The unguarded exhaust port was located at the end of a long channel on the surface of the Death Star.

Yet even the Death Star had a flaw. If a skilled pilot could fire torpedoes into a small exhaust shaft on the Death Star's surface, a chain reaction of explosions would blow up the entire starship. The Rebel Alliance sent their best pilots to reach the target. Luke Skywalker trusted in the Force and fired. A direct hit! Luke had managed to destroy the Empire's most terrible weapon.

Mastermind
One of the Emperor's leaders, Grand Moff Tarkin, was the mastermind behind the Death Star.

Rebel Victory

The brave Rebels refused to give up the fight against Emperor Palpatine and his Empire of evil. Although the Emperor commanded the biggest army in the galaxy, he was not invincible. The Rebels teamed up with a band of forest-dwelling creatures called Ewoks on the planet Endor. Together they overpowered the Emperor's stormtroopers and helped the Rebels' spaceships to launch a full-scale attack on the second Death Star.

Look out!
The Ewoks only used weapons made of wood, yet they managed to defeat the well-trained and well-armed stormtroopers.

Meanwhile onboard the Death Star, Luke battled for his life against the Emperor and Darth Vader. When Luke refused to turn to the dark side, the Emperor forced the father and son to fight. In the end, Luke could not kill Vader and when the Emperor tried to kill Luke, Vader turned against his Sith Master and threw him to his doom down a deep shaft.

Luke had proven that even those who have turned to the dark side still have good inside them that can be reached—if you only know how.

Vader unmasked
Luke lifted Vader's mask to gaze at the face of the father he had never known.

Glossary

Apprentice
A person who is learning a skill.

Blaster
A gun that fires a deadly beam of light.

Bounty hunter
A person who hunts criminals and other wanted people, in return for money.

Clone
An exact copy of another person.

Dark side
The part of the Force associated with fear and hatred.

Droid
A kind of robot.

Emperor
The leader of an Empire is called an Emperor. Palpatine is the Emperor who rules the Galactic Empire.

Empire
A group of nations ruled by one leader.

The Force
An energy field created by all living things.

Force lightning
One of the Sith's powers which involved firing deadly electricity from their fingers.

Galactic
Something from or to do with a galaxy.

Galaxy
A group of millions of stars and planets.

Jedi Council
The governing body of the Jedi order. The wisest Jedi, such as Yoda, sit on the Council.

Jedi Knight
A *Star Wars* warrior with special powers who defends the good of the galaxy. Anakin Skywalker, Luke Skywalker, and Ob-Wan Kenobi are all Jedi Knights.

Jedi Master
The most experienced Jedi of all.

Jedi order
The name of a group that defends peace and justice in the galaxy.

Jedi Temple
The Jedi headquarters where the Jedi Council meets and Jedi live, train, and work.

Lightsaber
A Jedi's or Sith's weapon, made of glowing energy.

Light side
The part of the Force associated with goodness, compassion, and healing

Rebel
Someone who opposes whoever is in power.

Republic
A nation or group of nations in which the people vote for their leaders.

Senate
The governing body of the Republic.

Senator
A member of the Senate. He or she will have been chosen (elected) by the people of his or her country.

Sith
Enemies of the Jedi who use the dark side of the Force.

Stormtroopers
Soldiers, many of them clones, who are loyal to Emperor Palpatine. They wear white armor.

STAR WARS
GALACTIC CRISIS!

Written by Ryder Windham

Darth Sidious

Palpatine

Sith Lord
Although he appears to be a trusted Senator, Palpatine is really the evil Darth Sidious.

Secret identity

A long time ago, in a galaxy far, far away, a mighty Republic existed. All the different planets who were part of the Republic agreed to work together to bring about peace. Large armies were not allowed. Instead, the noble Jedi Knights were the Republic's peacekeepers.

The Jedi got their power from the Force, an energy field generated by all living things. Their greatest enemies were the Sith Lords, who used the Force for evil.

One of the deadliest Sith Lords was Darth Sidious (SID-EE-US). This villain played a game. He was secretly a Sith, but he had another identity. He was also Senator Palpatine of the planet Naboo. Most people thought Palpatine was a kind man, but he was really a master politician who used people and events to achieve total power.

Palpatine was a member of the Galactic Senate, a place where Senators met to govern the Republic and discuss important matters.

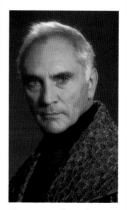

Senate leader
Supreme Chancellor Valorum is leader of the Senate. He has to keep order in the Senate and deal with corrupt politicians from many worlds.

Government
The Galactic Senate meets on the planet Coruscant (CORE-RUS-SANT). Senators from all over the galaxy meet here to discuss new laws and other matters.

Naboo threatened

Both Palpatine and Valorum
came from Naboo. Their world's
government was a democratic
kingdom, ruled by the elected
leader, Queen Amidala.
Naboo's human population did not
have an army, which made
them easy to invade.
Palpatine wanted to gain
more power. So he persuaded an
aggressive trading organization
called the Trade Federation
to try to conquer Naboo.
The Trade Federation was run
by aliens called Neimoidians
(NY-MOY-DEE-ANS) who
demanded that Amidala
surrender, but she refused.
Valorum knew that
some Senators would support
the invasion because the
Neimoidians had powerful
friends in the Senate.

Valorum wanted to help Naboo without alerting the Neimoidians. He secretly sent two Jedi Knights, Qui-Gon Jinn (KWY-GON JIN) and his apprentice, Obi-Wan Kenobi (OH-BEE ONE KEN-OH-BEE), to the planet. Valorum hoped the Trade Federation would leave Naboo as soon as the Jedi Knights arrived.

Qui-Gon Jinn

Obi-Wan Kenobi

Escape to Tatooine

The Neimoidians were fearful of the Jedi Knights but were even more afraid of Darth Sidious, who told them to kill the Jedi. Fortunately, Qui-Gon and Obi-Wan evaded the Neimoidians and escaped into Naboo's swamps.

Puppet leader
Neimoidian viceroy Nute Gunray appears to be in charge of the Trade Federation invasion, but he receives his orders from Darth Sidious.

Evil warrior
Darth Maul was trained by Darth Sidious. He uses a double-bladed lightsaber.

There, the Jedi befriended Jar Jar Binks, a Gungan. The Gungans lived partly on land and partly in underwater cities. The Gungans' leader, Boss Nass, gave the Jedi and Jar Jar a submarine so that they could travel under the water to rescue Queen Amidala.

The Jedi and Amidala left Naboo in a starship to inform the Senate of the invasion. The ship was damaged on the way, however, and they had to land on the planet Tatooine (TAT-OO-EEN).

Meanwhile, Darth Sidious sent his deadly apprentice, Darth Maul, to track down Amidala's ship.

Gungan boss
Boss Nass is leader of the underwater city Otoh Gunga. He doesn't trust humans because he believes they think that Gungans are less important than humans.

Jedi friend
Bungling Jar Jar eventually becomes a representative of Naboo.

103

Criminal world

Slave boy
The Republic's anti-slavery laws do not apply on Tatooine. Slaves Anakin and his mother, Shmi, are parted after Anakin wins his freedom.

Tatooine was not governed by the Republic but was controlled by criminals and slave traders. While seeking a replacement engine for Amidala's starship, Qui-Gon and Amidala met two slaves: young Anakin Skywalker and his mother, Shmi, who were owned by an alien junk dealer. After seeing that Anakin was unusually strong with the Force, Qui-Gon helped him to gain his freedom and leave Tatooine.

Although Darth Maul tried to capture Amidala, the Jedi delivered her safely to Coruscant, where she told the Senate of the invasion.

Top criminal
Jabba the Hutt is the top criminal on the planet Tatooine.

When the Senate failed to take immediate action, Palpatine convinced Amidala that most of the Senate—including Valorum—was weak and useless. Palpatine urged Amidala to support a vote to replace Valorum with a new leader.

Power struggle
On Coruscant, Palpatine encourages Queen Amidala to question Valorum's leadership, then puts himself forward as a replacement leader.

An alliance
For her own safety, Queen Amidala disguises herself as a royal handmaiden. She finally reveals herself to gain the trust of Boss Nass.

Fight for freedom

While the Senate prepared to decide Valorum's future, Qui-Gon and Obi-Wan escorted Amidala back to Naboo. Although her people had long lived separately from the Gungans, Amidala asked for help from their leader, Boss Nass. He soon realized that Amidala did not think of herself as better than him and that the time had come to defend their shared world. So he agreed to help her to stop the Trade Federation destroying everything that the Naboo and Gungans had worked so hard to build.

Battle of Naboo
Brave Gungan warriors fight hand-to-hand with the Trade Federation's remote-controlled battle droids.

Meanwhile, Darth Maul arrived on Naboo with a mission to assassinate the Jedi and Queen Amidala. Qui-Gon and Obi-Wan were soon engaged in a furious lightsaber fight with the Sith Lord.

Jedi versus Sith
The Jedi fight Darth Maul on Naboo. Only Obi-Wan will survive the battle.

Anakin saves Naboo

Having traveled to Naboo with the Jedi, young Anakin tried to stay out of trouble but wound up piloting a Naboo starfighter straight into the Trade Federation's Droid Control Ship. He destroyed the ship, which caused the battle droids to suddenly stop fighting, and ended the invasion.

Obi-Wan defeated Darth Maul, but not before the Sith Lord had left Qui-Gon mortally wounded. Qui-Gon's final request was for Obi-Wan to instruct Anakin in the ways of the Force.

Winning strike Anakin stops the Trade Federation's entire droid army by firing torpedoes into the Droid Control Ship.

As the Neimoidians were led away, Amidala learned that Palpatine had been elected as the new Supreme Chancellor. She had no idea that the invasion had been part of Palpatine's scheme to start a war in the Republic. Because she did not know, she and her friends happily celebrated what they believed to be their victory.

Yoda

A new regime
Now the Supreme Chancellor, Palpatine vows to bring peace to the Republic. Secretly, he is already planning another war.

Mace Windu

Jedi Council
Yoda and Mace Windu are both members of the Jedi Council, the ruling body of the Jedi Knights. They are reluctant to allow Obi-Wan to train Anakin to be a Jedi. But in the end they honor Qui-Gon's wish.

Lucky escape
Because
Amidala is
against a war,
she becomes
a target to
enemies who
hope to gain
from conflict.
An attack on
Amidala's
starship fails to
kill her because
she traveled in
disguise in
another ship.

Ten years later

Following the death of Darth
Maul, Darth Sidious took a new
apprentice, a traitorous Jedi Master
called Count Dooku.

Ten years after the Battle of
Naboo, Count Dooku led a group
of planets who wanted to leave
the Republic. These Separatists said
that the Republic was corrupt and
weak. This made it hard
for the Jedi to keep order
in the Republic, so
the Senate considered
creating an army.

Padmé Amidala continued to serve Naboo as a Senator when her term as queen had ended. She was against the building of an army. Shortly after Amidala arrived on Coruscant to vote against the creation of an army, an assassin destroyed her starship. Because the Separatists seemed to want a war with the Republic, Amidala suspected that Count Dooku was behind the attack.

Extended reign
Supreme Chancellor Palpatine secretly organizes a series of crises to stop elections from taking place. This means he can remain as leader longer than is usually allowed.

Double life
Count Dooku is secretly working with Darth Sidious. His other, evil identity is as Darth Tyranus, a Sith Lord.

Padmé in danger

The Jedi Council asked Obi-Wan Kenobi and Anakin Skywalker to protect Senator Amidala. They hoped to stop any further attempts on her life. Anakin had grown into a man in the years since Padmé had last seen him, but, as a Jedi, he still had much to learn from Obi-Wan.

After a second attempt on Padmé's life, Obi-Wan caught the would-be assassin, a female hunter called Zam Wesell. But before she could tell the Jedi who had hired her, she was killed by a toxic dart fired by a mysterious man.

The killer escaped using a jetpack. Only later would Obi-Wan discover that he was Jango Fett. Meanwhile, Padmé was still in danger.

Jango Fett

Clawdite killer
Zam Wesell looks like a human, but she is in fact a Clawdite. This alien species can change its form at will.

Armored man
Zam Wesell is killed by the man who hired her, a bounty hunter named Jango Fett. He makes his living by killing or capturing people for a reward.

113

Surprise at Kamino

Useful friend
Dexter Jettster
is a four-armed
alien who owns
a diner in a
seedy part of
Coruscant
known as
Coco Town.
The cook is
happy to help
his pal,
Obi-Wan.

After Obi-Wan and Anakin reported to the Jedi Council, Mace Windu instructed Anakin to take Padmé to the safety of Naboo. Meanwhile, Obi-Wan visited his old friend, Dexter Jettster, who was a weapons expert. Dexter identified the assassin's dart as a weapon from the planet Kamino.

Obi-Wan set off for Kamino, hoping to track down the armored bounty hunter. When he arrived, he was met by tall aliens who were expecting a Jedi to visit them.

The aliens, Kaminoans (KAM-IN-OH-ANZ), wanted to show Obi-Wan the army they had been building for the Republic—an army of clones. These clone soldiers were identical copies of a ferocious human bounty hunter.

The Kaminoans told Obi-Wan that a Jedi Master called Sifo-Dyas had asked them to build the clone army ten years earlier. This puzzled Obi-Wan because he'd never heard of the army. However, to gain their trust, he pretended to the Kaminoans that he knew about what they were doing.

Obi-Wan later discovered that Palpatine himself sent the mysterious Sifo-Dyas to Kamino to commission the vast clone army.

Clone makers
The Kaminoans are experts at producing clones.
They sometimes make money by creating clones for beings from other worlds.

The clone army

The Kaminoan Prime Minister, Lama Su, showed Obi-Wan the enormous buildings where clone soldiers were made. They were born in special birth areas and trained to be obedient soldiers from a young age. The Kaminoans had already raised and trained 200,000 clone troopers and another million soldiers were nearly ready.

Obi-Wan soon learned that every clone was an exact copy of a bounty hunter named Jango Fett. The Jedi quickly asked to meet him. At Jango's apartment, Obi-Wan met the hunter and his clone "son," Boba. Jango said he didn't know the mysterious Jedi who ordered the army and said that a man named Tyranus had recruited him.

Clone troopers
Each clone is totally obedient and will follow orders without question. Despite their human appearance, the clones have few emotions.

Although Obi-Wan did not yet have solid evidence, he suspected that Jango Fett was responsible for the attempts to kill Senator Amidala.

Military exercises
When they are not sleeping or eating, the clone troopers train to perfect their fighting skills and be ready for combat.

Same son
Ten-year-old Boba Fett is an exact copy of Jango Fett. Unlike the other clones, he has not been altered to be obedient.

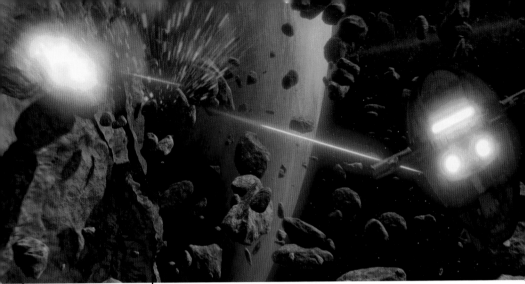

Space chase
Obi-Wan
chases Jango
Fett's ship
through a maze
of dangerous
rocks in space.
Jango fires at
Obi-Wan's
ship, but he
cannot shake
off the Jedi.

Secret plans

Obi-Wan told the Jedi Council about the clone army on Kamino. The Council instructed Obi-Wan to bring Jango Fett to Coruscant. Before he could, Obi-Wan was attacked by Jango, who then fled with Boba in their ship, *Slave I.*

Obi-Wan followed Jango. The bounty hunter's trail ended on the planet Geonosis (GEE-OH-NO-SIS). Millions of droid soldiers were being made there in a huge factory. Obi-Wan then spotted Count Dooku persuading alien business leaders to join the Separatists.

Tambor Watt, leader of the Techno Union.

Unified powers
Count Dooku wins over the greedy business organizations. He tells them that he will make it easy for them to trade anywhere in the galaxy.

Shu Mai, head of the Commerce Guild.

The Separatist movement was now renamed the Confederacy of Independent Systems and had its own army of droid soldiers.

Obi-Wan transmitted this information to Anakin but was captured by enemy droids. After Anakin received the information and sent it to the Jedi Council, he and Padmé raced to Geonosis to rescue Obi-Wan.

Weapons of war
The insectlike Geonosians make weapons. They build the droid soldiers for the Confederacy.

Jedi prisoner
Count Dooku
tries to gain
Obi-Wan's
trust by
revealing
information
about the Sith.
He hopes that
by doing this,
he will learn
why Obi-Wan
is on Geonosis
and possibly
persuade
the Jedi Knight
to work
with him.

Taken prisoner

After he was captured on
Geonosis, Obi-Wan was taken to
a prison cell and trapped within
a force field. Count Dooku pretended
to be friendly when he visited the Jedi
and tried to convince him that
they didn't have to be enemies.

Dooku informed Obi-Wan that
the Senate was under the control
of a Sith Lord called Darth Sidious,
who had betrayed the Trade
Federation at the Battle of Naboo.

Dooku claimed he'd tried to tell the Jedi Council about the evil Darth Sidious, but they'd refused to listen. He invited Obi-Wan to join him so that they could work together to destroy the Sith.

Although Obi-Wan believed in the possibility of a Sith Lord in the Senate, he suspected Dooku was not telling the whole truth. Obi-Wan refused to join Dooku and remained a prisoner. After Anakin and Padmé arrived on Geonosis to rescue Obi-Wan, they were also captured.

No deal
Dooku promises to free Padmé and the Jedi if Naboo joins the Confederacy. Despite the threat of execution, Padmé refuses to surrender her world.

Execution arena

On Coruscant, the Jedi Council had informed the Senate of Obi-Wan's discovery of the clone army on Kamino and the Confederacy activity on Geonosis. The Senate would not approve the use of the clone army before a Confederacy attack. So Palpatine took advantage of Padmé's absence by tricking Naboo's other representative, Jar Jar Binks, into helping him.

Jar Jar proposed that the Senate should grant emergency powers to Palpatine. This meant that the Chancellor could deal with the Confederacy threat without having to wait for the Senate to vote.

Jar Jar tricked
Jar Jar Binks wants to save his friends on Geonosis. So he helps Palpatine gain the power to create an army for the Republic. Jar Jar doesn't realize he's been tricked by the Sith Lord.

No way out? Padmé, Anakin, and Obi-Wan are to be killed by deadly beasts in the arena.

The Senate agreed and allowed Palpatine to activate the clone army.

Back on Geonosis, Obi-Wan, Padmé, and Anakin were sentenced to death in a giant execution arena. Suddenly 200 Jedi and thousands of clone troops rescued them.

Then, on the fields outside the arena, the mighty army of clone troops, led by the Jedi, went into battle with the Confederacy's droids.

Last resort Although the Jedi prefer peaceful solutions to war, they lead the clone troops into battle on Geonosis.

In secret

As the Republic's army began to overwhelm the droids, the Archduke of Geonosis gave the designs for a super-weapon to Count Dooku. The Sith Lord then raced for his starship. Anakin was badly wounded attempting to stop and capture Count Dooku. He failed, and Dooku escaped.

Many Jedi died at the Battle of Geonosis. After the survivors returned to Coruscant, Anakin took Padmé back to Naboo.

Super-weapon
The Geonosians provide Count Dooku with designs for what will be the biggest super-weapon the galaxy has ever known— the Death Star.

The deceivers
The Dark Lords of the Sith, Darth Sidious and Count Dooku, never wanted the Confederacy to win the Battle of Geonosis. Their goal is to start a war in the hope that it will allow them to take total control of the Republic.

Hollow victory
Obi-Wan at first believes the Battle of Geonosis is a victory for the Republic. Yoda disagrees, as he knows the conflict is only the beginning of the Clone Wars.

Anakin's fellow Jedi had no idea that he and Padmé had fallen in love or that Dooku had also traveled to Coruscant to report to his master, Darth Sidious.

Secret wedding
On Naboo, Padmé and Anakin marry in a ceremony witnessed by R2-D2 and C-3PO. Marriage is forbidden for Jedi. So the event will remain a secret even to Anakin's friend, Obi-Wan.

Dooku betrayed

About three years after the Battle of Geonosis, the Clone Wars continued. The Confederacy's General Grievous abducted the Republic's leader, Supreme Chancellor Palpatine (who is secretly the Sith Lord, Darth Sidious).

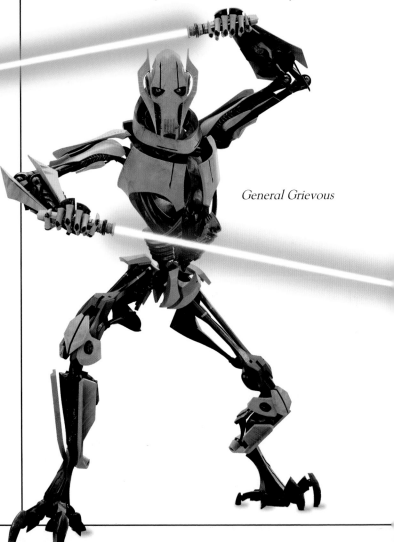

General Grievous

Jedi killer
General Grievous is the Supreme Commander of the Confederacy's droid armies. Count Dooku trained the droid in the art of lightsaber combat. Grievous also takes orders from Darth Sidious.

Jedi battle
Count Dooku
and Anakin
take part in
a ferocious fight
with their
lightsabers.

Obi-Wan and Anakin—helped
by R2-D2—followed Grievous and
got on board his flagship. Following
a fight with Grievous, the Jedi found
Palpatine held captive by Count
Dooku. Dooku briefly overcame
Obi-Wan but was brutally defeated
by Anakin, who was urged on by
the Chancellor. Dooku believed
the Chancellor had a plan that
would protect him. He was shocked
when Palpatine ordered Anakin to
execute him.

Although Grievous escaped
into space, the Jedi successfully
returned Palpatine to Coruscant.

A test
Palpatine
commands
Anakin to kill
Count Dooku.
The Sith Lord
is testing
Anakin's
loyalty. He is
also seeing if
Anakin has
the potential to
become his new
Sith apprentice.

Split loyalties

Shortly after Anakin's return to Coruscant, Padmé told him she was pregnant. Anakin believed this was happy news until a series of nightmares made him worry that Padmé might die.

Meanwhile, Padmé became more concerned about the future of the Republic. Chancellor Palpatine had made many changes to the laws of the Republic to deal with one crisis after another. These changes had increased his power and meant that he had remained Chancellor longer than was usually allowed.

Worried Senators
Padmé, Bail Organa, and Mon Mothma are among the Senators who realize that Palpatine is becoming a threat to democracy.

Padmé

Bail Organa

Mon Mothma

The Jedi Council was
also suspicious of Palpatine.
When the Chancellor made Anakin
his representative to the Council,
they agreed so that Anakin could spy
on Palpatine. Anakin hoped that he
would now become a Jedi Master and
was angry when the Council said
he was not ready.

Building trust
Palpatine
tells Anakin
important
information to
make him feel
like a friend.

**Caught in
the middle**
Anakin learns
that the Jedi
Council wants
him to spy on
Palpatine.
He feels torn
between his
loyalties to the
Chancellor and
to the Council.

Duping Anakin
Palpatine
creates
a stronger bond
wth Anakin
by making him
suspicious of his
dearest friends,
Obi-Wan and
Padmé.

Darth Vader

The Jedi Council learned that
General Grievous had been seen on
the planet Utapau. They sent Obi-
Wan and two clone brigades to find
him. Meanwhile, Palpatine revealed
to Anakin that he was a Sith Lord.
He made Anakin believe that only
the dark side of the Force could
keep Padmé free from harm.

After Obi-Wan defeated
Grievous, Mace Windu and three
other Jedi confronted Palpatine.

They demanded an end to the Clone Wars. Anakin had now convinced himself that the Jedi had become his enemies. He decided to turn to the evil dark side of the Force and join Palpatine. Together, he and Palpatine killed the four Jedi Knights.

Palpatine made Anakin his apprentice. He called the new Sith Lord Darth Vader and instructed him to kill the remaining Jedi on Coruscant, then get rid of the Confederacy leaders who were hiding on the planet Mustafar.

Failed mission
Mace Windu realizes that Palpatine has no intention of ending the war. He and three other Jedi attempt to arrest Palpatine. The Jedi do not know that the Sith Lord is prepared to kill them.

Total power

After Palpatine had gotten rid of his Jedi enemies on Coruscant, he ordered the clone commanders throughout the galaxy to turn on the Jedi Knights. As the clones had been trained to obey their supreme leader's orders without question, they did as they were told.

Surprise attack
The clone troops had always fought on the side of the Jedi. So the Jedi are totally unprepared when the clones open fire on them.

Yoda and the Wookiees
On the planet Kashyyyk, Yoda helps defend the Wookiees from an invasion of Confederacy droids. After an attempt on Yoda's life, the Wookiees Tarfful and Chewbacca help him escape.

Chewbacca

Many Jedi died, but Yoda and Obi-Wan managed to escape the assault and reunite with their ally, Senator Bail Organa of Alderaan. Returning to Coruscant, they learned that Palpatine was calling himself Emperor. He now had complete power of the Republic.

Soon, Yoda and Obi-Wan discovered that Palpatine was indeed the Dark Lord of the Sith and that Anakin was his apprentice, Darth Vader. They were determined to stop the murderous Sith Lords.

Evil Emperor
Chancellor Palpatine tells the Senate that the Jedi were responsible for an attempt on his life that left him scarred and deformed. No one dares to stop him from declaring himself Emperor.

Finding evidence
On Coruscant, Yoda and Obi-Wan view a recording that shows them Anakin has betrayed the Jedi and turned to the dark side.

Fiery planet
Mustafar is
a dark,
frightening
world covered
with volcanoes.
People live
on the sides
of great
mountains.

Attack on Mustafar

Searching for Anakin, Obi-Wan went to Padmé's apartment. Padmé was relieved to see that Obi-Wan had survived the attack but refused to believe his claim that Anakin had turned to evil. Anakin had told Padmé that he would be traveling to Mustafar to fight the Confederacy. But she told Obi-Wan that she didn't know where he was.

After Obi-Wan left, Padmé and C-3PO boarded her spaceship and set out for Mustafar, unaware that Obi-Wan had hidden in the ship.

End of the resistance
By having Anakin kill the Confederacy leaders, Palpatine destroys the only organized resistance to his new Empire.

Obi-Wan hoped that Padmé might lead him to Anakin.

On Mustafar, Anakin carried out Palpatine's instructions and killed the Confederacy leaders. Moments after Palpatine learned of Anakin's deed, Yoda attacked the self-appointed Emperor. Despite Yoda's mastery of the Force, he was unable to destroy the Sith Lord.

Yoda versus the Emperor
Yoda and Palpatine battle with their lightsabers in the Senate.

ceased to exist when he became Darth Vader. But it still upsets him to have to fight his own apprentice.

confronted her husband, Anakin, about the terrible things he'd done. But Anakin claimed that his actions had brought peace to the Republic.

He said that he could use his powers to overthrow Palpatine and rule the galaxy. Padmé tried to make him understand that she still loved him despite his actions. However, when Anakin saw Obi-Wan come out of the Naboo ship, he became angry and choked Padmé with the Force. Though he didn't kill her, she collapsed.

Anakin and Obi-Wan lit up their lightsabers and began a fierce duel that continued through several levels of the volcanic world. After severely wounding Anakin, Obi-Wan left him for dead. Just as the Emperor arrived on Mustafar, Obi-Wan fled into space with Padmé.

Vader lives
Palpatine senses that Darth Vader is in danger. He travels to Mustafar on his Imperial shuttle to help him. Palpatine rushes Vader's body back to a medical center on Coruscant.

Helpful droids
R2-D2 and C-3PO bring the injured Padmé back to her ship.

Birth and death

Padmé was taken to the remote asteroid Polis Massa. There she gave birth to twins that she named Luke and Leia. Moments after their birth, Padmé died. It was quickly decided that the twins should be hidden, to keep them safe from the Sith. Bail Organa agreed to adopt Leia, and Obi-Wan promised to deliver Luke to Tatooine.

When Darth Vader awoke in a medical center on Coruscant, he found his damaged body repaired.

Jedi twins
Luke and Leia never knew their mother, but both will meet Darth Vader years later.

Suit of evil
Darth Vader's body is so damaged that he has to rely on an armored suit's life-support system to breathe.

He was now partly a robot and wore a suit of black armor. Soon, Vader recovered and was able to join his Master to begin work on the Death Star. He did not know that Padmé had given birth to his son and daughter.

More lies
The Emperor allows Vader to believe that he killed his beloved Padmé because Palpatine wants to destroy any trace of human feeling left in his apprentice.

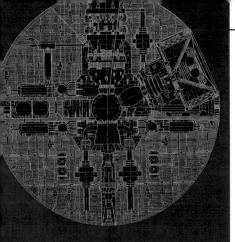

The future

The Death Star would take many years to finish. The Emperor believed that every planet in the galaxy would fear the planet-shattering station and give in to his rule. Thinking himself all-powerful, he was not concerned with the location of the surviving Jedi.

Yoda traveled to Dagobah, an unpleasant swamp planet that was full of meat-eating life-forms. The small Jedi Master would remain on Dagobah for the rest of his life.

Death Star
When the immense battle station is finished, it will be able to destroy entire planets.

On Tatooine, Obi-Wan left Luke with Anakin's stepbrother, Owen Lars, then headed off to make his own home on the desert world. He would continue his training and study of the Force until the day when Bail Organa would call him back to duty for one last mission.

Glossary

Abduct
To capture
someone and take
them away.

Alien
A creature that
is not human
or animal.

Apprentice
A young person
who is learning
a skill.

Assassinate
To murder.

Asteroid
A large space rock.

Betray
To break a promise.

Bounty hunter
Someone who
captures criminals
for money.

Clone
An exact copy of
a living being.

Confederacy
A union of different
independent groups
or nations.

Corrupt
To change from
good to bad.

Democracy
A nation
in which
the people vote
for their leaders.

Diplomacy
Talking rather
than fighting.

Election
When people vote
for their rulers.

Empire
Group of nations
ruled by an
Emperor, who has
total power.

Federation
Groups that unite
because they have
the same aims.

Government
The leaders who
rule a nation.

Invasion
The sending of an
army into a place
to take it over.

Kingdom
A nation ruled by
a king or queen.

Mortally
Describes something
that will cause death.

Politician
Someone who helps
govern a nation.

Potential
Being able to
do something in
the future.

Representative
Someone who
stands in for
someone else.

Republic
A nation or group
of nations in which
the people vote for
their leaders.

Resistance
Fighting against
something.

Separatist
A person or group
that wants to leave
a larger group.

Slave
Someone owned by
someone else.

Trade
The buying and
selling of goods.

Traitorous
Describes someone
who has betrayed
their friends or cause.

✦STAR WARS✦
EPIC BATTLES

Written by Simon Beecroft

Jedi Knights
The Jedi use a mysterious energy called the Force. Jedi Knights carry glowing lightsabers to defend themselves.

What side are you on?

A long time ago, in a galaxy far, far away, a great and peaceful Republic existed. Each planet, large or small, made its voice heard in a huge Senate building on the capital planet, Coruscant. The Jedi Knights defended peace and justice everywhere. They ensured that arguments between planets were sorted out without violence or war.

Battle droids
The Trade Federation built many millions of machine-soldiers called battle droids. Each battle droid carries a deadly blaster weapon.

Sadly, this peace was about to be smashed. A greedy business organization called the Trade Federation created an army and began to invade planets, starting with a small world called Naboo. As the conflict grew, the Republic later deployed its own army. With the galaxy at war, both sides learned too late that they had been manipulated by a deadly Sith Lord!

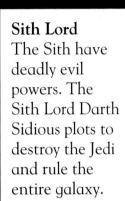

Sith Lord
The Sith have deadly evil powers. The Sith Lord Darth Sidious plots to destroy the Jedi and rule the entire galaxy.

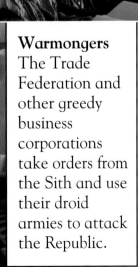

Warmongers
The Trade Federation and other greedy business corporations take orders from the Sith and use their droid armies to attack the Republic.

The Sith were the greediest beings in the galaxy. The leader was called Darth Sidious and he was secretly controlling the Trade Federation. He wanted it to start a war that would put him in power as Emperor. He fooled everyone by pretending to be a kindly politician called Senator Palpatine. Palpatine became leader of the Senate, took control of the Republic's army, and forced every planet to obey him.

Hired hands
Sith Lords often hire assassins, spies, and bounty hunters to do their dirty work for them. Bounty hunters are skilled hunters who kidnap people for a fee.

A few brave people refused to accept Palpatine's evil Empire. They were called the Rebel Alliance—and they set out to free the galaxy.

This is the story of the Emperor's rise to power and his downfall at the hands of the brave-hearted Rebels. It is a story of great struggles on land and in space. From all-out attacks to deadly duels and fights with savage beasts, these battles are epic!

Rebels at the ready
Luke Skywalker, his twin sister Princess Leia, Han Solo, and the Wookiee Chewbacca all fight for the Rebel Alliance.

Legendary land battles

The galaxy first erupted into violence when the Trade Federation invaded Naboo. This peaceful planet was home to the Naboo people and a water-dwelling species called the Gungans. Two Jedi were sent to investigate: Qui-Gon Jinn and Obi-Wan Kenobi. With help from the Gungans, the Jedi rescued the Naboo Queen, Padmé Amidala.

Vile leaders
The Trade Federation's cowardly leaders land on Naboo only after their battle droids have captured the royal palace.

The Jedi took Queen Amidala to Coruscant to ask the Senate for its help. But the Senate was all talk and no action. Amidala would have to free her planet herself!

She and the Jedi returned to Naboo and battled their way to the hangar where their spaceships were housed. Then Amidala led an attack on the royal palace, fighting many battle droids. Elsewhere, the Gungans fought a battle-droid army. Now the Naboo pilots had to destroy the Trade Federation ship that was controlling the battle droids.

Swift strike
Qui-Gon slices a deadly battle droid in two as he helps Queen Amidala escape from her planet.

Back-up droid
Droideka are even more deadly than battle droids. They carry twin blaster weapons.

Return to Naboo
Qui-Gon Jinn and Obi-Wan Kenobi lead the attempt to recapture Queen Amidala's palace.

Gungan soldiers face the might of the Trade Federation's droid army.

Boss Nass
Queen Amidala asks the Gungan ruler, Boss Nass, to help her fight the invaders.

The deadly land battle between the Gungan army and the massed ranks of battle droids took place on a wide-open grassy plain. At first the Gungans were very clever. They activated special machines carried by their giant swamp lizards. These machines generated an energy bubble that protected the Gungan army from high-speed airborne missiles.

But the Gungans did not realize that battle droids could walk right through their shield. Now the two armies battled each other inside the shield. The Gungans fought bravely but could not hope to win against an endless supply of battle droids. It would take a space battle above Naboo to shut down the droid army.

Binoculars

Atlatl

Electropole

War weapons
Gungans use a variety of unusual weapons that fire balls of explosive energy called plasma. They hurl these balls into the air with catapults and throwing sticks called atlatls.

Energy shields
Gungan soldiers carry glowing energy shields into battle to protect themselves from blaster bolts fired by battle droids.

151

New leader
The Neimoidian leaders are joined by a powerful new ally, the former Jedi, Count Dooku.

Wheel droids
Sinister hailfire droids roll into battle on giant hoop wheels, while Republic gunships prepare to strike from above.

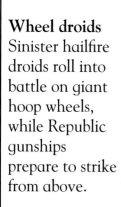

After the Republic learned that its enemies were creating huge droid armies, it was tricked into using a ready-made army to defend itself. Its Army consisted of millions of clone troopers—each clone was an identical copy of a single ultimate soldier. This hastily assembled army first saw action on a planet called Geonosis.

Jedi generals
At the battle of Geonosis, Yoda and many other Jedi have to become military generals for the first time.

Advance guard
Clone troopers blast their way toward the enemy, using special sight systems in their helmets to see through the dense smoke on the battlefield.

The droid armies attacked the Jedi in a large arena on Geonosis. When clone troopers joined the fray, led by Jedi Master Yoda, the battle spread outside the arena. Many Jedi and clone troopers were killed, but finally the droids and their masters retreated. This was the first battle of the famous Clone Wars.

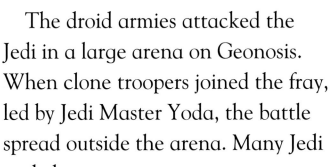

Tarfful
One of the
Wookiee leaders
is called Tarfful.
When the
Republic's clone
troopers,
wheeled tanks,
and walking
guns go into
battle against
the droids,
Tarfful and
the Wookiees
are right
alongside them.

Droid armies
attacked everywhere.
One of the biggest battles
took place on Kashyyyk. This
planet was home to tall, furry
creatures called Wookiees. The
Wookiees and the Republic army
fought on land and sea. But just as
victory was in sight, it all went
wrong. The Republic did not know
that their clone troopers had been
brainwashed to switch sides when
they received a special signal.

Tanks roll in
On Kashyyyk, many Trade Federation tanks roll over land and water with battle droids mounted on the sides.

When the clones received the signal, Order 66, they turned their weapons on their Jedi generals. The clones took orders only from the Sith. When Darth Sidious became Emperor, the clone troopers became his personal army, known now as stormtroopers. The Empire was born.

Assassination
When the Sith signal is received, every clone commander turns on the Jedi. Nearly all the Jedi leaders are killed. Aayla Secura is assassinated while fighting on the fungi planet, Felucia.

Walking tanks
The Empire's terrifying walking tanks, called AT-ATs, advance across the snow toward the Rebel base.

Great land battles took place in the time of the Empire, too. Many brave individuals joined the Rebel Alliance and fought against the Empire, though they had few weapons, vehicles, or other resources. The Emperor and Darth Vader put much of the Empire's military might toward crushing the Rebel Alliance.

Front line
The Rebels try to hold off the advancing AT-ATs with their heavy guns.

Rebel hangar
The Rebel base is a converted ice cave, with a massive hangar for vehicles.

Darth Vader discovered that the Rebels had built a secret base on the ice planet Hoth. His troops attacked it with great force. He sent in giant walking tanks called AT-ATs. The Rebels tried to hold off the AT-ATs for as long as they could, and even managed to destroy two of them. But eventually they were forced to flee and find another hiding place.

Enter Vader
Sith Lord Darth Vader enters the Rebel base, which is now a smoking ruin. He is flanked by stormtroopers equipped for missions in sub-zero conditions.

Scout trooper
Imperial scout troopers on flying speeder bikes chase down the Rebels when they land on Endor.

After the defeat at Hoth, the Rebels hid all over the galaxy. Palpatine hatched a plan to draw them out. He had once built a huge super-weapon called the Death Star, which the Rebels had destroyed. Now he built a second Death Star, knowing the Rebels would try to stop him. Then he would blow the Rebel fleet out of the sky.

Battle in the forest
Stormtroopers, backed up by a walking AT-ST cannon, do battle with Han and Chewbacca.

The Death Star was protected by a shield generator on the forest moon of Endor. A team of Rebels led by Luke Skywalker, Princess Leia, Han Solo, and Chewbacca went to Endor to destroy the generator. The Rebels faced a large Imperial army, but they were helped by natives called Ewoks. Together they suceeded in destroying the shield generator, and then the Rebel fleet was able to attack the Death Star.

Ewok attack
Small, determined Ewoks hurl rocks at stormtroopers in their well-planned attacks.

Rebel team
Han tries to break into the generator bunker while Leia holds off advancing stormtroopers.

Space battles

Many of the biggest battles in the galaxy took place in space. When the Trade Federation invaded Naboo, its massive battleships surrounded the planet. While the conflict raged on the ground, a handful of Naboo ships managed to take off and fly toward the battleships.

Feared fleet
Deadly Trade Federation vulture droid ships emerge from the ring-shaped Droid Control Ship.

Rookie pilot
Anakin is whisked into the space battle when the autopilot engages in the starfighter he is hiding in.

One of the Naboo ships was flown—at first, accidentally— by a nine-year-old boy called Anakin Skywalker. Anakin had Jedi abilities and was a superb pilot, although he had never flown a starship before. He managed to enter the Trade Federation's Droid Control Ship and fire torpedoes into its reactor room, escaping in his starfighter as the ship exploded. Anakin's incredible feat saved Naboo.

Brave strike
Starfighters avoid deadly laser blasts.

Blown away
The Control Ship sends instructions to every battle droid. When it is destroyed, the droids stop fighting.

Close combat
A Naboo starfighter narrowly avoids a direct hit as the Droid Control Ship fires at oncoming Naboo ships.

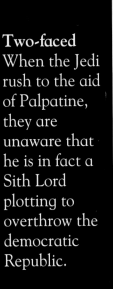

Jedi team
Anakin and
Obi-Wan fly
side-by-side in
their fast
Interceptors.

Two-faced
When the Jedi
rush to the aid
of Palpatine,
they are
unaware that
he is in fact a
Sith Lord
plotting to
overthrow the
democratic
Republic.

The space battle
above Naboo was just
the beginning. Worse was
yet to come. A full-scale
war broke out between the
Republic and the droid armies.
Their battle fleets met in a gigantic
space conflict above Coruscant.
The leader of the Republic, Supreme
Chancellor Palpatine, had been
kidnapped, and two Jedi set off to
rescue him: Obi-Wan Kenobi and
Anakin Skywalker.

Direct hit
Both sides lose some of their spaceships in the explosive space battle above Coruscant.

The Jedi dodged enemy fire and landed on the cruiser in which Palpatine was being held. After freeing Palpatine, Anakin had to pilot the cruiser to a crash landing after a Republic ship tore it apart.

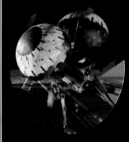

Tiny but deadly
Small buzz droids attach themselves to the side of Obi-Wan's ship to inflict damage with their cutting arms.

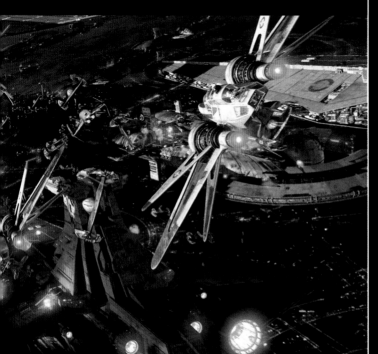

Deadly sky
Republic warships engage droid fighters large and small in the raging battle above Coruscant.

Distinctive ship
Jango pilots one of the deadliest ships in the galaxy, *Slave I*. It is armed with weapons and lethal surprises.

Young ally
Jango Fett's son, Boba, travels in *Slave I* with his father, learning from his every action.

Some space battles involved many ships, like the battle above Coruscant. In others, just two ships engaged in a duel called a dogfight. When Obi-Wan was on the trail of a dangerous villain called Jango Fett, the chase led into a highly lethal asteroid field. Any collision with these floating rocks would be fatal. Jango tried to lose Obi-Wan by blasting rocks close to the Jedi's ship.

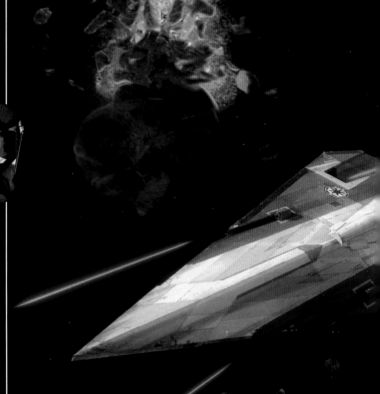

Obi-Wan was a skilled pilot and he dodged each explosion. Then Jango steered his ship around an asteroid so he was now the one pursuing Obi-Wan. He fired a special seeker missile, but Obi-Wan faked his ship's explosion. When Jango saw the blast, he believed that Obi-Wan had been killed, but the clever Jedi was really hiding on one of the asteroids.

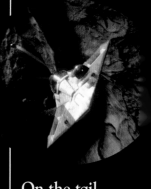

On the tail
Seeker missiles can home in on fast-moving objects so they are hard to shake off.

Jedi pilot
Even though Obi-Wan says he is not keen on flying, his piloting skills are superb.

Trusty ship
The *Falcon* is battle scarred from its many space adventures.

Another ship that has been in many dogfights is the *Millennium Falcon*. Piloted by Han Solo and Chewbacca, the ship could outrun most enemy craft. If the going got tough, the *Falcon* could jump to lightspeed, enabling it to vanish instantly and reappear somewhere far away.

Under pressure
A giant Star Destroyer chases the *Falcon* while Imperial TIE-fighters blast it with laser fire.

Heat of battle
Piloted by Han's old friend and rival, Lando Calrissian, the *Falcon* evades Imperial fighters at the second Death Star.

Han Solo flew the *Falcon* in many daring raids against the Imperial fleet. Once, he landed right on the hull of an enormous Imperial Star Destroyer to evade its radar. Another time, he made the seemingly suicidal decision to fly into an asteroid field to shake off Imperial fighters. The daring plan worked and he escaped with his life.

Hot shot
Han Solo was once a reckless smuggler. Then he joined the Rebel Alliance and eventually he even married Princess Leia.

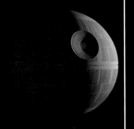

Death Star
The moon-sized Death Star had the firepower to destroy an entire planet.

Strike force
Rebel teams of X-wing and Y-wing starfighter pilots fly from their base on Yavin 4 toward the Death Star.

Rebel space battles

The Rebel Alliance was dedicated to opposing the oppressive rule of the Empire, despite being desperately under-equipped. The Empire had a massive starfleet, but the Alliance made do with a small number of battle-worn starfighters.

The Alliance learned that the Empire had built an enormous battle station called the Death Star. Stolen plans showed a flaw: If a Rebel starfighter could fire a torpedo into a tiny exhaust port, the chain reaction would destroy the battle station.

The Rebel pilots boldly launched an assault on the Death Star from their base on the planet Yavin 4. The Empire was not expecting an attack on its deadly superweapon. One Rebel pilot was skilled enough to strike the target: Luke Skywalker. The Death Star exploded—and the Rebels scored their first major victory against the Empire.

Enemy ships
Two Imperial ships chase the Rebel pilots along a narrow trench on the Death Star.

Hot shot
Luke hits the exhaust port that leads into the heart of the battle station's colossal reactor.

Rebel leader
Admiral Ackbar
is the loyal
Commander
of the Rebel
fleet at the
Battle of Endor.

*The battle rages
around the half-
completed
Death Star.*

The Battle of Endor was the final showdown between the Rebels and the Empire. Part of the conflict took place above the forest moon of Endor, where the Empire was building a second Death Star. While a team of Rebels landed on Endor's moon to disable the shield generator protecting the Death Star, the entire Rebel fleet came out of hiding to launch a final, do-or-die attack.

A Rebel ship crashes into the bridge of an Imperial Star Destroyer, while Rebel B-wings fly in formation nearby.

At one point in the battle, Rebels targeted the Empire's Star Destroyers, hoping the Death Star would hold fire to avoid hitting its own ships. The battle turned when a damaged Rebel ship crashed into a Super Star Destroyer. With the shield down, Rebel ships could attack the Death Star's power plant, causing a fatal explosion.

Direct assault
The *Millennium Falcon* flew through the Death Star's superstructure to detonate the battle station's power plant.

Lightsaber clashes

Since ancient times, the lightsaber has been the chosen weapon of the Jedi Knights. Until the Sith emerged from hiding, the Jedi used their lightsabers only as defence against blasters and other weapons. But the Sith also used lightsabers. Now the Jedi faced opponents armed with their own traditional weapon.

Surprise attack
Darth Maul first appears on the desert planet Tatooine. He ambushes Jedi Qui-Gon Jinn.

Sith opponent
On Naboo, it takes two skilled Jedi to hold back Darth Maul's double-bladed lightsaber.

Final strike
Qui-Gon meets
Maul in a clash
that would spell
the Jedi's doom.

*Obi-Wan leaps to avoid a low
parry from Maul's glowing blade.*

During the Battle of Naboo,
Darth Sidious's Sith apprentice,
Darth Maul, emerged. Maul's
appearance was terrifying, with face
tattoos, yellow eyes, and several
horns. Darth Maul attacked Jedi
Qui-Gon Jinn and Obi-Wan Kenobi.
He managed to kill Qui-Gon. Obi-
Wan was devastated but he fought
on until he had defeated his Sith foe.

Jedi in trouble
On the edge of
a deep shaft,
Maul nearly
triumphs over
Obi-Wan. But
the Jedi will not
give up until he
has defeated the
savage Sith.

173

Sith blade
Dooku's lightsaber blade is red, as all Sith blades are.

Captured Jedi
On Geonosis, Count Dooku wants Obi-Wan Kenobi to join him as a Sith.

With Darth Maul dead, Sith Lord Darth Sidious had to train a new apprentice. He chose a former Jedi called Count Dooku. The elegant, commanding Dooku left the Jedi Order to become a Sith. Sidious taught him to use the destructive dark side of the Force.

At the Battle of Geonosis, Dooku fought a great Jedi Master, Yoda. They clashed in a blur of lightsaber blows. Dooku used the Force to throw massive objects. This time, he managed to escape.

Jedi against Sith
The Jedi fight Dooku
onboard the cruiser.

Dooku next
faced Obi-Wan
and Anakin on
the cruiser where
Palpatine (really Darth
Sidious) was being held prisoner.
Dooku knocked Obi-Wan
unconscious. But he was unaware of
Sidious's masterplan: He wanted
Anakin to kill Dooku and replace
him as his new Sith apprentice.

Bad influence
Palpatine
encourages
Anakin to reject
his Jedi training
and unleash his
anger to kill
Dooku in
cold blood.

Count Dooku was not the only lightsaber-wielding foe the Jedi would meet during the Clone Wars. They also confronted a half-machine, half-living creature called Grievous, who was general of the droid armies. Grievous had also been trained by Count Dooku in lightsaber combat. He liked to steal lightsabers from the Jedi he killed, and hoped to add Obi-Wan and Anakin's weapons to his collection.

Lethal general
On Utapau, Obi-Wan finds that General Grievous is a dangerous opponent in lightsaber combat.

Utapau chase
Grievous on his wheelbike and Obi-Wan on a fast varactyl lizard trade blows on the planet Utapau.

Furious foe
Grievous's two arms can split into four, giving the Jedi extra lightsabers to dodge and parry. Obi-Wan will shear off some of these extra limbs.

But not this time! The daring Jedi fought off Grievous's bodyguards and escaped the general's clutches.

Grievous next met Obi-Wan on the planet Utapau. Wielding four lightsabers, Grievous unleashed a brutal assault. A high-speed chase across the planet surface led to a final showdown—and Grievous's dramatic demise in a ball of fire.

Explosive end
Obi-Wan uses a blaster to fire the fatal shots that enflame Grievous.

Lost cause
On the volcano planet called Mustafar, Obi-Wan realizes that Anakin is no longer a Jedi.

Sith opponent
Anakin, now named Darth Vader, unleashes his Sith powers against Obi-Wan Kenobi.

Ever since Senator Palpatine first met Anakin Skywalker, he knew the young Jedi had great powers. He also perceived Anakin's unruly emotions and knew he could be turned to the Sith cause. After he had encouraged Anakin to kill Dooku, Palpatine revealed that he was a Sith, and Anakin joined him, becoming Darth Vader. Then Palpatine made Vader believe Obi-Wan was against him.

Anakin's eyes gleam with anger as Obi-Wan defeats him in battle.

Darth Vader and Obi-Wan fought on the volcano planet Mustafar. Obi-Wan gained the upper hand and left Vader for dead. But Emperor Palpatine rebuilt Vader in black armor. Then Vader took his place beside the Emperor.

Darth Vader fought Obi-Wan once more, taking the Jedi's life. It wasn't until he battled with his own son that Vader was able to reject the Sith and the dark side.

Deadly rematch
Vader and Obi-Wan meet in combat for the last time on the first Death Star.

Father-son duel
Vader wants his son Luke to join him as a Sith, but Luke refused.

Cruel Master
Palpatine enjoys the fight between his Sith accomplice, Dooku, and his accomplice-to-be, Anakin.

Sith unmasked
Palpatine displays his Sith lightsaber skills in the fight with Mace Windu.

For a long time, the most evil Sith Lord in the galaxy went by the name of Palpatine. Pretending to be a friend to the Republic, he secretly masterminded a war that made him the cruel ruler of the galaxy.

The Jedi realized too late that Palpatine was really a Sith Lord named Darth Sidious. High-ranking Jedi Master Mace Windu lost his life attempting to stop the Sith schemer.

Palpatine had hidden his Sith lightsaber until Mace confronted him.

Even Yoda was unable to defeat the Emperor in lightsaber combat. In the end, Sidious's own ally, Darth Vader, sided with Vader's son, Luke Skywalker. Vader turned against his Sith Master and threw Emperor Palpatine to his death.

Explosive clash
The two most powerful users of the Force's light and dark sides clash in a spectacular duel in the Senate building on Coruscant.

Lightning strike
Sidious fires deadly Sith lightning at Luke. But Vader will be unable to stand by and let his son die.

Famous showdowns

Jango finds that
Obi-Wan is hard
to hit with a blaster.

Airborne foe
Jango uses his
jetpack to soar
above Obi-Wan
on Kamino.

Final end
In the arena
battle on
Geonosis, Jedi
Mace Windu
strikes the fatal
blow that ends
Jango's life.

Even before the Clone Wars, the
galaxy was not entirely peaceful.
Many criminals thrived, including
bounty hunters, who captured or
attacked people for a price. The best
bounty hunter in the galaxy was
named Jango Fett. Jango wore sleek
armor and carried many
weapons. He clashed with
Obi-Wan on a watery
planet called Kamino.

Though Jango escaped, the Battle of Geonosis would be his undoing. In the combat, Mace Windu struck Jango down with a powerful thrust from his lightsaber blade.

Jango's son Boba witnessed his father's death. Boba became a bounty hunter like his father. He came to work for Darth Vader and the notorious gangster Jabba the Hutt, among others. With Vader's help, Boba captured Han Solo and delivererd him to Jabba, who wanted Han for unpaid debts. A fierce battle ensued when Luke Skywalker and his friends rescued Solo from Jabba.

Battle-scarred
Boba Fett had many famous showdowns in his career as a bounty hunter. But he meets his match in the battle at Jabba's palace.

Deadly duel
Boba clashes with Luke, but a lucky strike from Han will knock the bounty hunter out of the battle.

Enter the beast
The three-horned reek enters the arena on Geonosis for a showdown with the human prisoners.

Jedi Knights, Rebels, and other defenders of freedom in the galaxy have had many showdowns with bounty hunters, assassins, and vile gangsters. They have also faced some nightmarish beasts.

On the planet Geonosis, Obi-Wan, Anakin, and Padmé Amidala were sentenced to public execution—by savage beasts.

Bared teeth
A soldier prods the nexu into the arena with a spear, where it bears its fangs in anticipation of fresh meat.

Obi-Wan faces the fearsome acklay in the Geonosis arena.

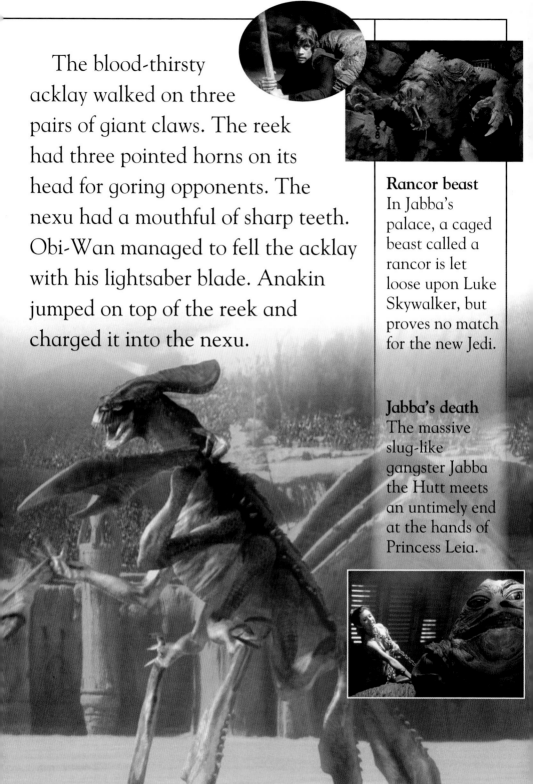

The blood-thirsty acklay walked on three pairs of giant claws. The reek had three pointed horns on its head for goring opponents. The nexu had a mouthful of sharp teeth. Obi-Wan managed to fell the acklay with his lightsaber blade. Anakin jumped on top of the reek and charged it into the nexu.

Rancor beast
In Jabba's palace, a caged beast called a rancor is let loose upon Luke Skywalker, but proves no match for the new Jedi.

Jabba's death
The massive slug-like gangster Jabba the Hutt meets an untimely end at the hands of Princess Leia.

A new era

At last—victory for the Rebel Alliance! The deaths of Emperor Palpatine and Darth Vader, and the destruction of the second Death Star, meant that the Empire was doomed. Peace and justice would soon be restored to the galaxy. The good news spread quickly and people rejoiced.

Father and son reunited
Luke looks at his father's true face for the first time, revealed beneath Darth Vader's helmet.

Forest celebration
In Endor's forests, Rebels and Ewoks celebrate the destruction of the terrible second Death Star that had threatened all of their lives.

The Rebel Alliance established a New Republic to replace the Empire. But troubles continued. Hundreds of planets that had accepted the Emperor's rule needed to be won over. Many loyal Imperial officers continued to attack the New Republic with remnants of the Imperial fleet. For Luke Skywalker, Han Solo, Princess Leia, and their allies, a new era had begun but the epic battle was not over yet.

Good times
Above the gigantic skyscrapers on Coruscant, fireworks light up the skies in celebration of the defeat of the evil Empire.

Glossary

Alien
A creature from outer space.

Apprentice
A person who is learning a skill.

Asteroid
A rock that floats in space.

Blaster
A gun that fires a deadly beam of light.

Clone
An exact copy of another person.

Dark side
The part of the Force associated with hatred.

Death Star
A moon-sized superweapon developed by the Empire.

Emperor
The leader of an Empire is called an Emperor. Palpatine is the Emperor who rules the Galactic Empire.

Empire
A group of peoples ruled by one leader.

The Force
An energy field created by all living things.

Force lightning
A Sith power, which involves firing deadly electricity from fingertips.

Galaxy
A group of millions of stars and planets.

Jedi Knight
A *Star Wars* warrior with special powers who defends the good of the galaxy.

Jedi Master
A high-ranking Jedi who has exceptional skills in using the Force.

Jedi Order
The name of the group that defends peace and justice in the galaxy.

Lightsaber
A Jedi's or Sith's sword-like weapon, with a blade of glowing energy.

Light side
The part of the Force associated with goodness, compassion, and healing

Lightspeed
A special kind of travel that allows a spaceship to cross vast distances of space in an instant.

Parry
To ward off a strike from a lightsaber or other sword-like weapon.

Reactor
A device in spaceships used to generate power for travel.

Rebel
Someone who opposes their government or ruler.

Republic
A nation or group of nations in which the people vote for their leaders.

Senate
The governing body of the Republic.

Senator
A member of the Senate. He or she will have been chosen (elected) by the people of his or her country.

Shield
An invisible protective barrier around a spaceship, planet, or other object.

Sith
Enemies of the Jedi who use the dark side of the Force.

Index